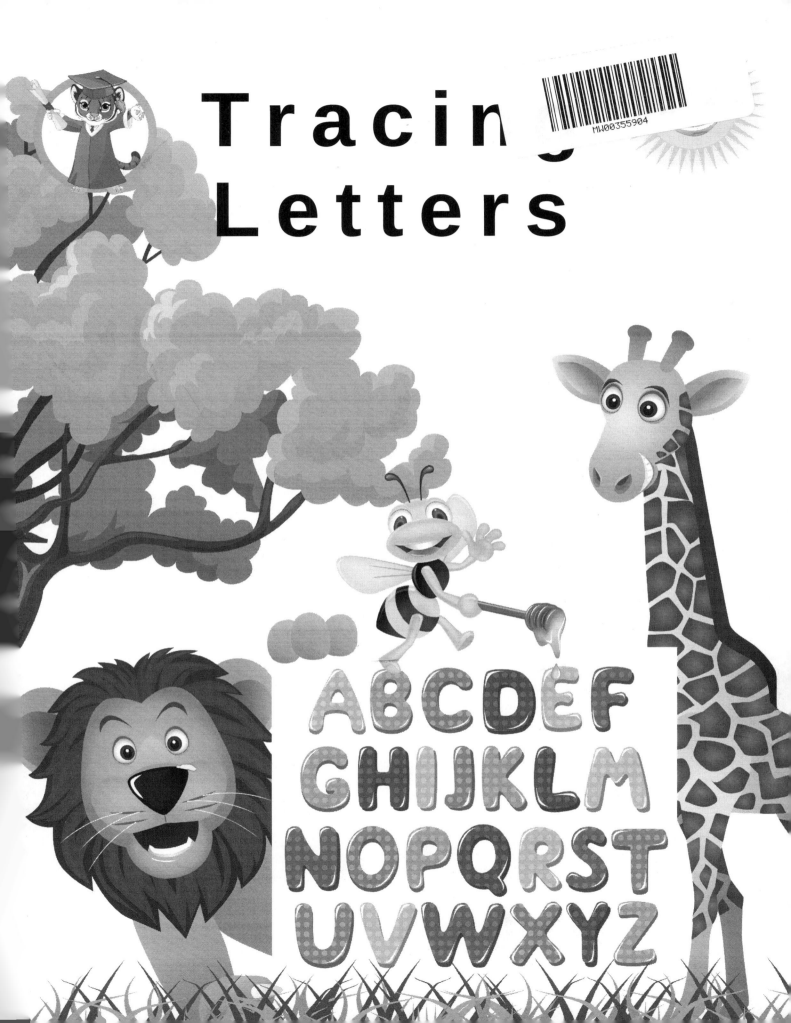

Tracing Letters

Pencil Position

Before your students begin writing, ensure that they are holding their pencils correctly.

Left Hand   Right Hand

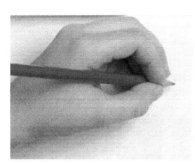   

- The fingers should be relaxed and slightly curved.
- The tips of the thumb, pointer finger, and middle finger should rest lightly on the pencil, approximately where the paint begins.
- The pencil should rest on the side of the hand between the thumb and pointer finger.

Note: Younger students sometimes benefit from larger pencils. If your student has difficulty gripping a smaller pencil, consider allowing your student to use one of these larger writing utensils.

Directions

Tracing Letters is a fun workbook designed for the youngest writers, teaching students proper letter formation by teaching them to trace the letters of the alphabet.

- Part one of this book covers the letters of the alphabet and their sounds.
- Part two reviews the alphabet and encourages children to trace words.

Directions along with scripted questions are given to assist parents and teachers as they introduce the letters and the letter sounds. The italicized words given in the LESSON section include the answers to the scripted questions given in the QUESTIONS TO ASK section.

Also, because children of this age enjoy coloring, black and white illustrations are included. In addition to being fun, the act of coloring helps children to strengthen the muscles in their fingers and hands and enables children to master handwriting faster.

Note: By design this book primarily introduces the short vowel sounds.
Note: Included are reproducible alphabet charts which you may copy.

ISBN-13: 978-1-940282-82-4

Connect the dots. What letter did you make?

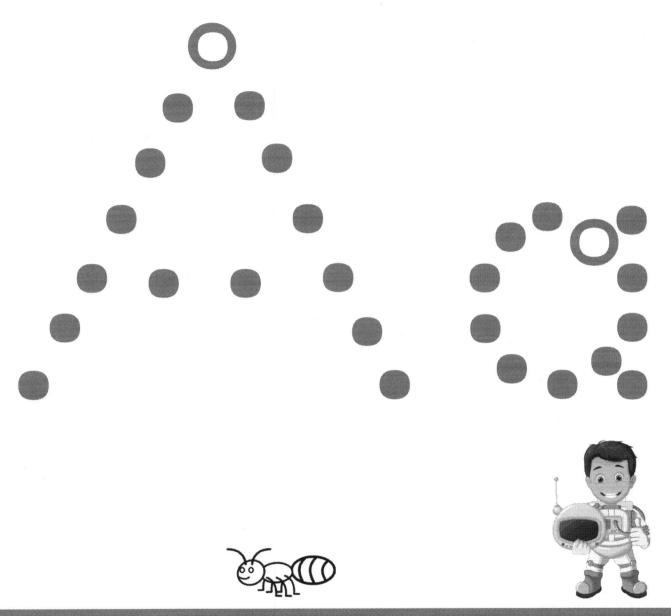

QUESTIONS TO ASK:

1. What kind of bug begins with the letter A and likes to eat your food?
2. What do you call a person that flies in a spaceship?
3. What juicy red or green fruit begins with the letter a?
4. What sound does the letter Aa make?

Bb

LESSON

➤ Introduce the name and **sound** of the letter B. Read the italicized words.
   Answers: *(b sounds like /b/ as in banana, bear, bed, birthday, and butterfly)*

➤ Have your student repeat the letter sound several times.

➤ Have your student trace the uppercase and lowercase letters.

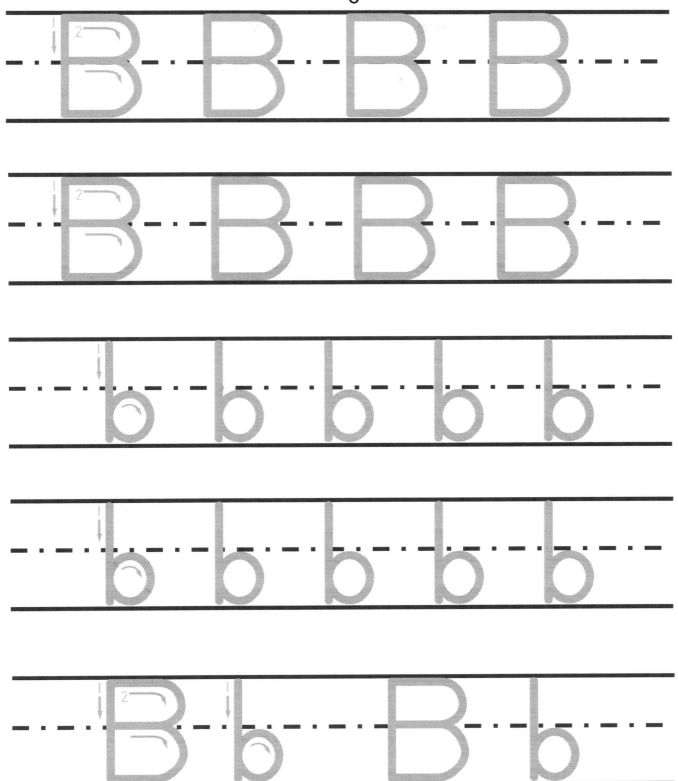

Connect the dots. What did you make?

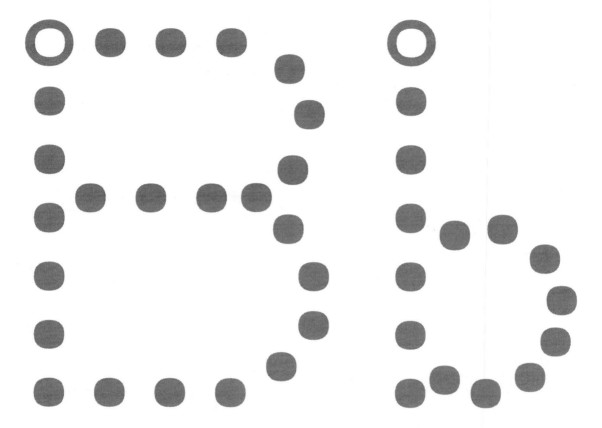

QUESTIONS TO ASK:

1. What is a yellow fruit that monkeys eat?
2. What big hairy animal lives in the woods and likes honey?
3. What do you sleep in at night?
4. What sound does the letter B make?

Connect the dots. What did you make?

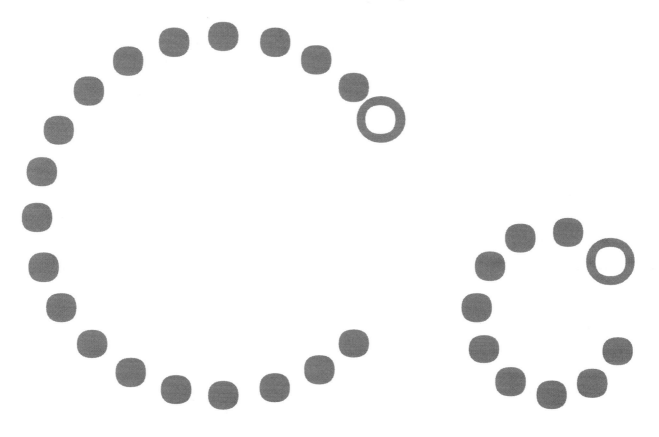

QUESTIONS TO ASK:

1. What large animal lives in the desert and has humps on its back?
2. Which animal meows?
3. When we are thirsty, what do we drink out of that starts with the letter C?
4. What sound does the letter C make?

Dd

➢ Introduce the name and sound of the letter D. Read the italicized words.
   Answers: *(d sounds like /d/ as in dog, doctor, duck, and dig)*

➢ Have your student repeat the letter sound several times.

➢ Have your student trace the uppercase and lowercase letters.   .

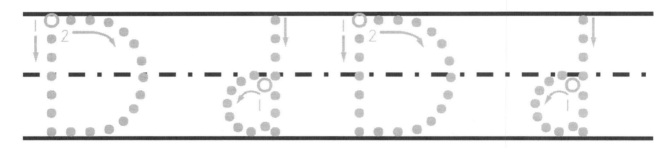

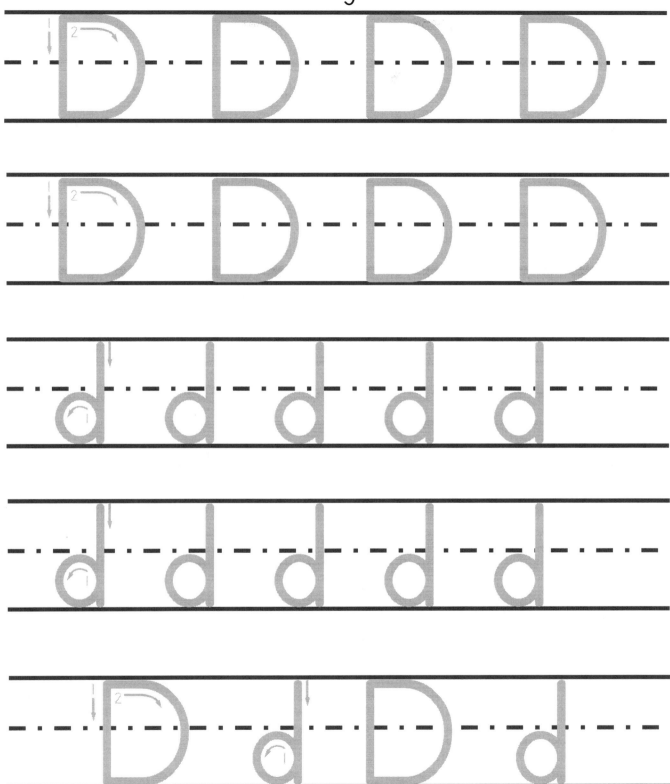

Connect the dots. What did you make?

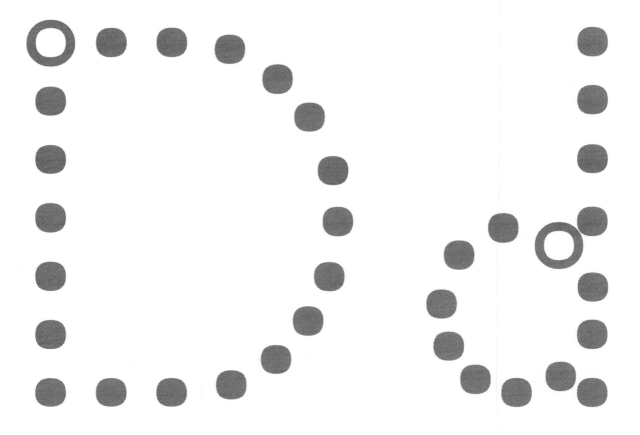

QUESTIONS TO ASK:

1. Who takes care of you when you are sick?
2. Name two animals that begin with the letter D.
3. What do you do with a shovel?
4. What sound does the letter D make?

Ee

LESSON

➢ Introduce the name and short vowel sound of the letter E. Read the italicized words.
   Answers: *(e sounds like /ĕ/ as in egg, elephant, and exercise)*

➢ Have your student repeat the letter sound several times.

➢ Have your student trace the uppercase and lowercase letters.

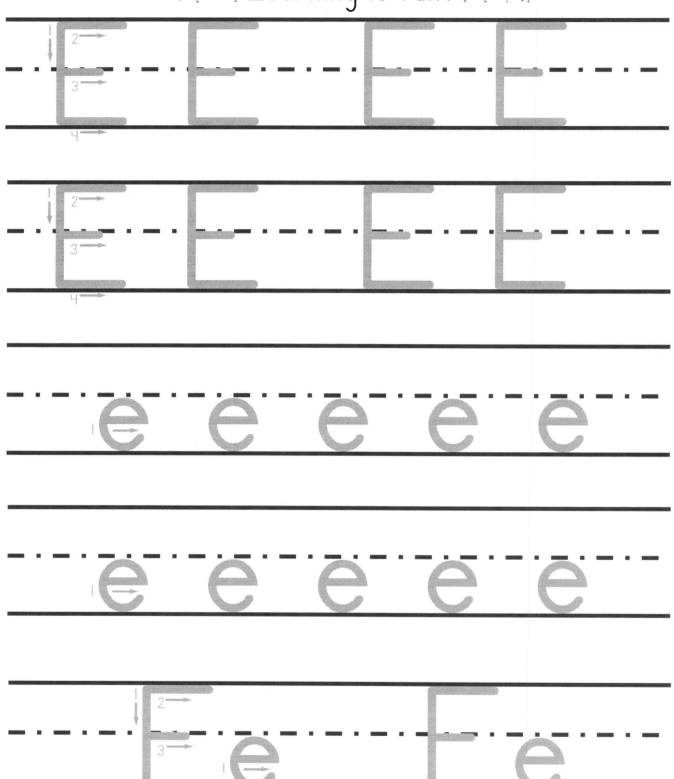

Connect the dots. What did you make?

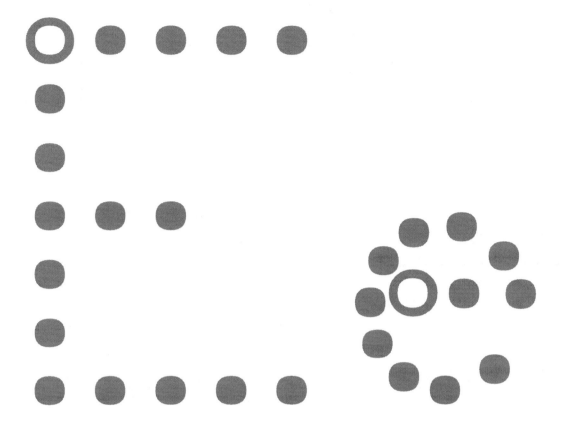

1. What do chickens lay?
2. What do we call activities such as running, jumping, and climbing? We do them to stay healthy.
3. Name a large animal that has a really long trunk?
4. What sound does the letter E make?

F f

LESSON

➢ Introduce the name and sound of the letter F. Read the italicized words.
   Answers: *(f sounds like /f/ as in fish, frog, fox, and foot)*

➢ Have your student repeat the letter sound several times.

➢ Have your student trace the uppercase and lowercase letters.

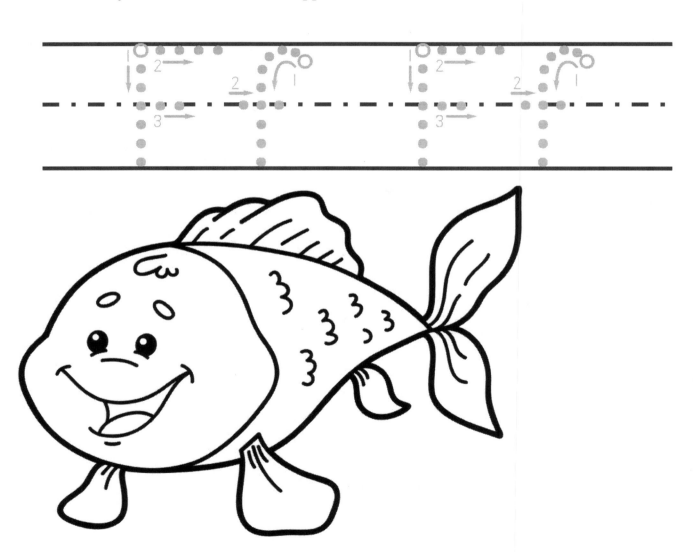

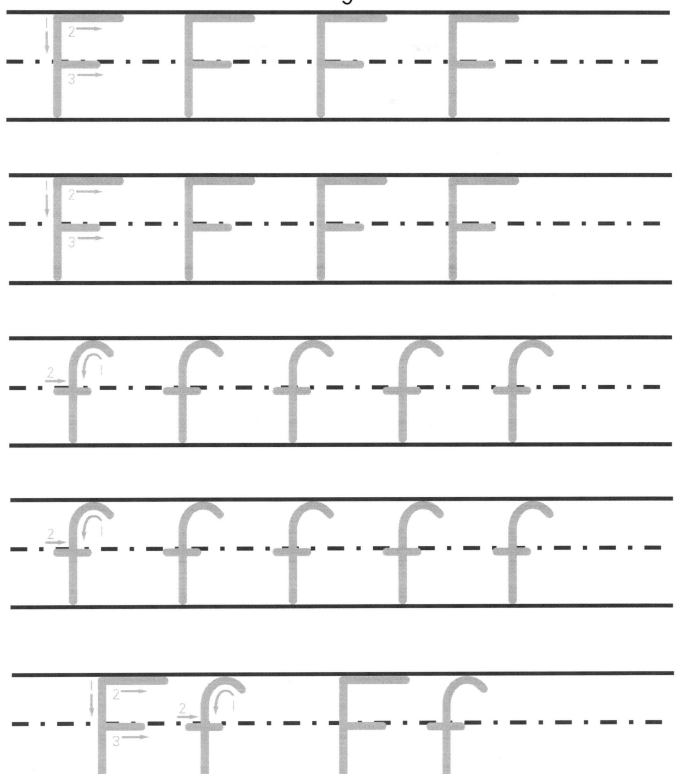

Connect the dots. What did you make?

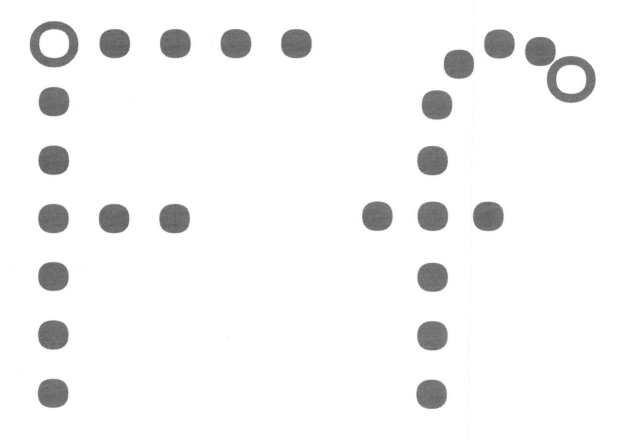

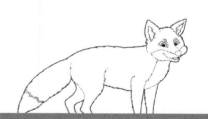

QUESTIONS TO ASK:

1. Name an animal that lives in the water. It begins with the letter F.
2. What are the names of two animals that start with the letter F?
3. Name a part of your body that you walk with?
4. What sound does the letter F make?

Gg

LESSON

➤ Introduce the name and hard g sound of the letter G. Read the italicized words.
  Answers: *(g sounds like /g/ as in girl, garden, grass, green, and gift)*

➤ Have your student repeat the letter sound several times.

➤ Have your student trace the uppercase and lowercase letters.

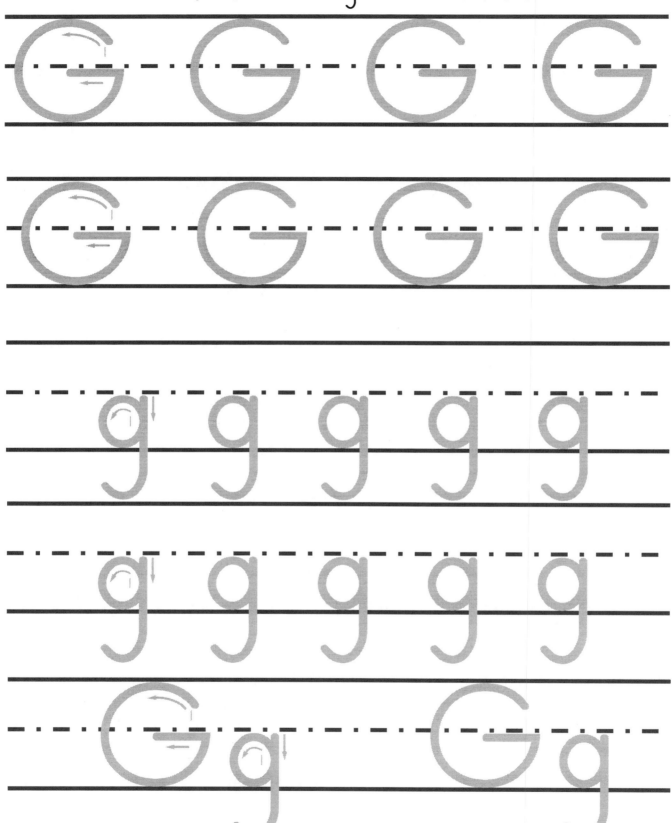

Connect the dots. What did you make?

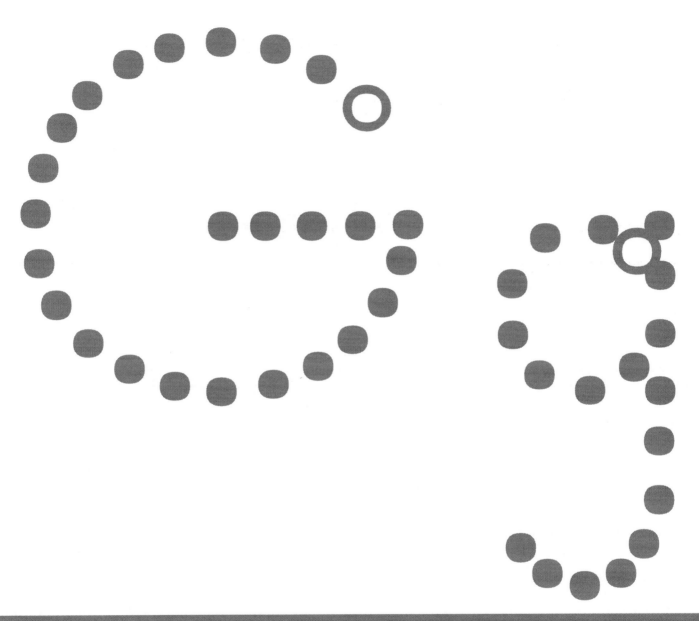

QUESTIONS TO ASK:

1. What is another word for birthday "present" that begins with G?
2. If someone grows flowers in their yard, they have a flower _____?
3. What is a color that begins with the letter G?
4. What is the sound of the letter g?

Hh

LESSON

➢ Introduce the name and sound of the letter H. Read the italicized words.
  Answers: *(h sounds like /*h*/ as in horse, hat, hand, and hotdog)*

➢ Have your student repeat the letter sound several times.

➢ Have your student trace the uppercase and lowercase letters.

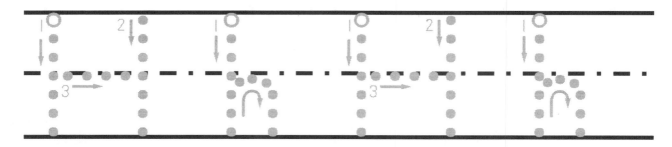

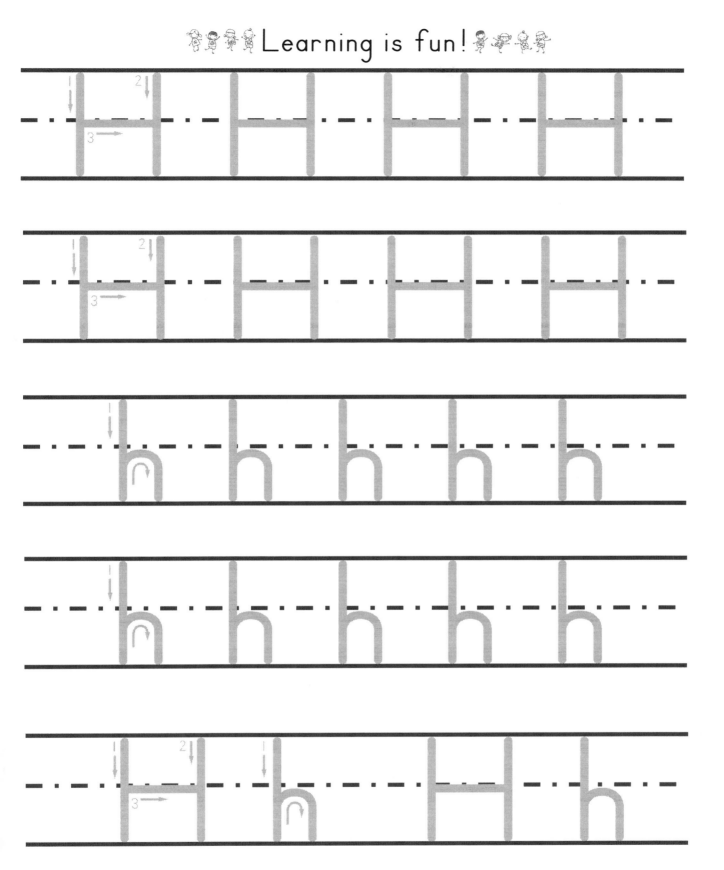

23

Connect the dots. What did you make?

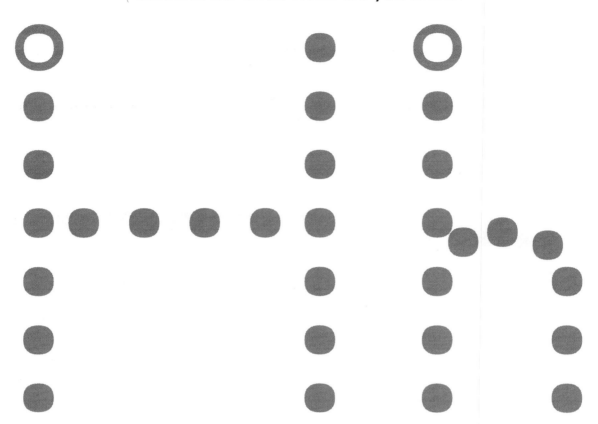

QUESTIONS TO ASK:

1. Name a food that begins with the letter H.
2. What part of your body do you write with?
3. What is the opposite of cold?
4. What sound does the letter H make?

I i

LESSON

➢ Introduce the name and short vowel sound of the letter I. Read the italicized words.
Answers: *(i sounds like /ĭ/ as in igloo, itch, inch, and in)*

➢ Have your student repeat the letter sound several times.

➢ Have your student trace the ŭppĕrcăsĕ and lowercase letters.

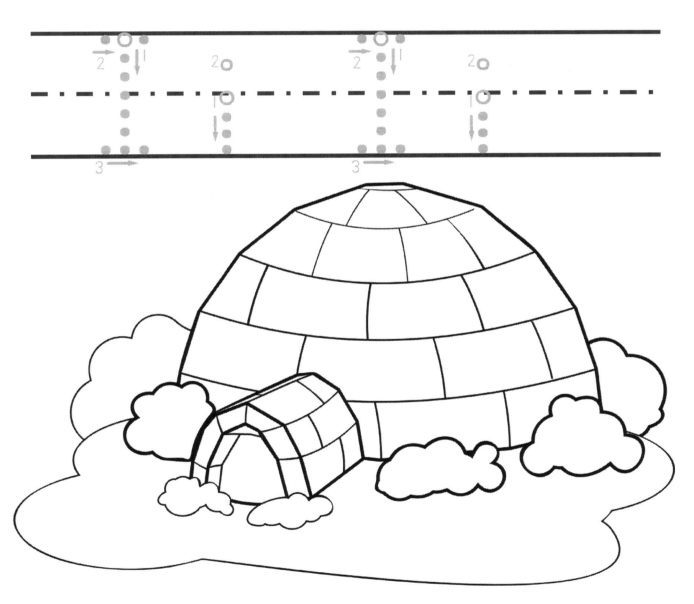

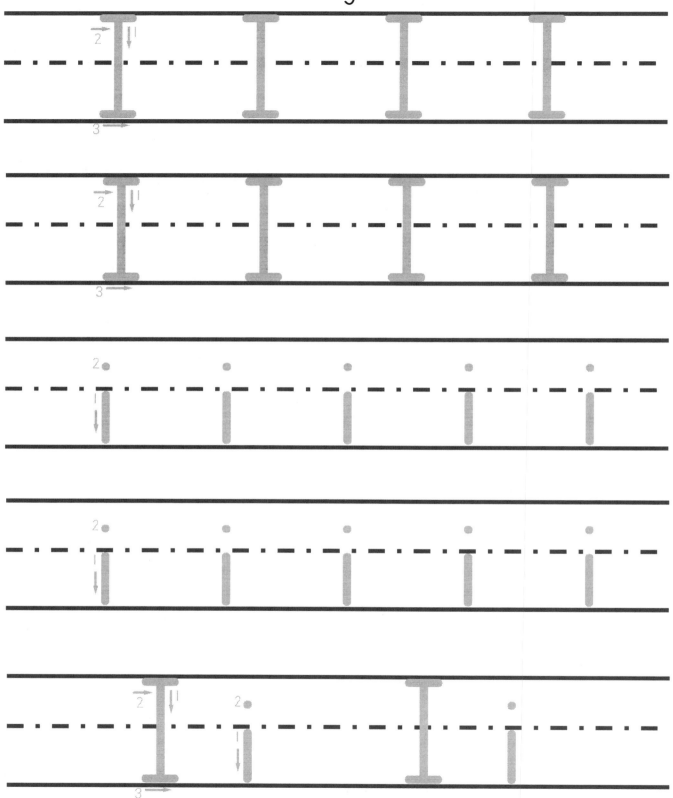

Connect the dots. What did you make?

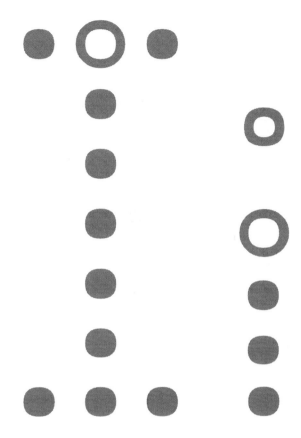

QUESTIONS TO ASK:

1. What type of house is made of snow?
2. How does a mosquito bite make your skin feel?
3. What is the opposite of out?
4. What sound does the letter I make?

in

27

Jj

LESSON

➢ Introduce the name and sound of the letter J. Read the italicized words.
   Answers: *(j sounds like / j / as in jellyfish, jump, jet, and jam)*

➢ Have your student repeat the letter sound several times.

➢ Have your student trace the uppercase and lowercase letters.

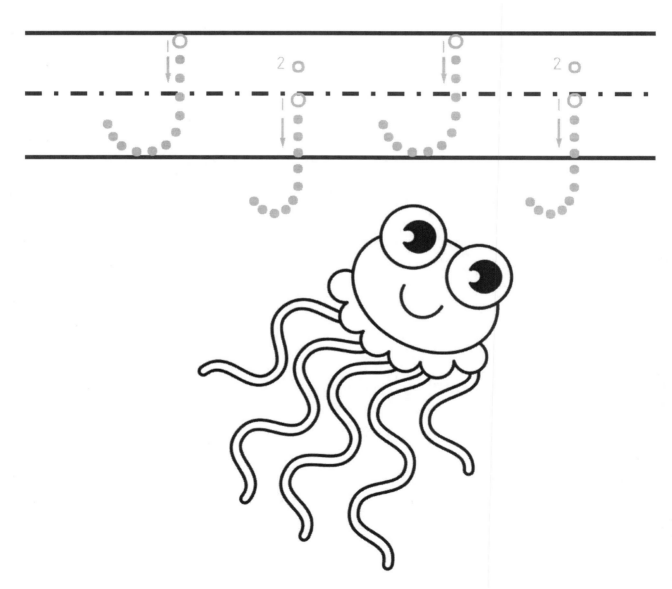

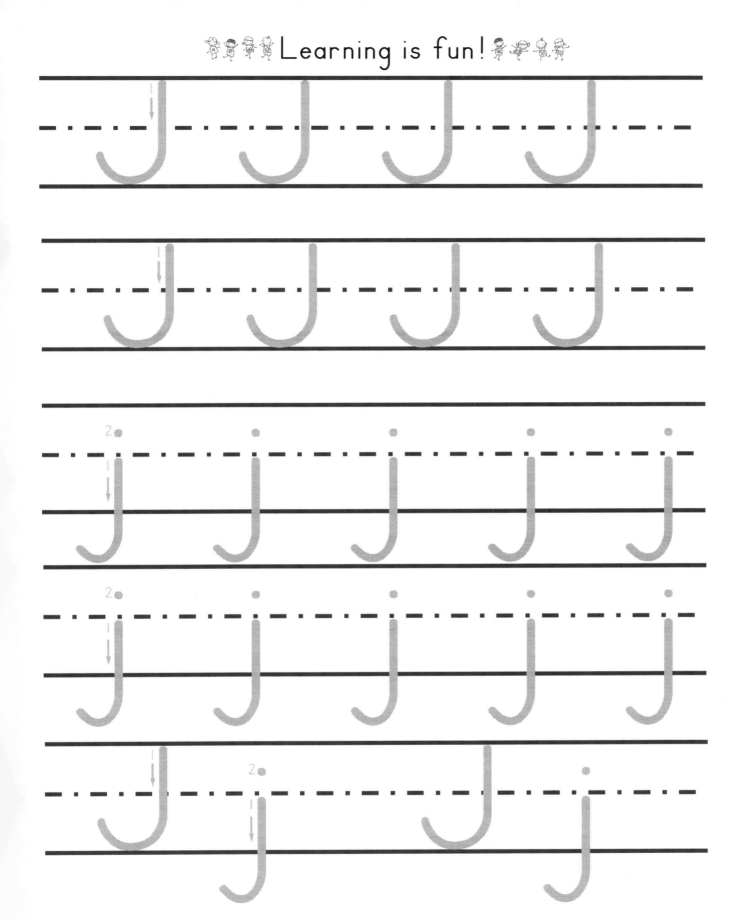

Connect the dots. What did you make?

QUESTIONS TO ASK:

1. What do you do on a trampoline?
2. What is another word for airplane that begins with J?
3. Name a person you know whose names begin with J.
4. What sound does the letter J make?

Kk

LESSON

➤ Introduce the name and sound of the letter K. Read the italicized words.
   Answers: *(k sounds like /k/ as in king, kiss, and kangaroo)*

➤ Have your student repeat the letter sound several times.

➤ Have your student trace the uppercase and lowercase letters.

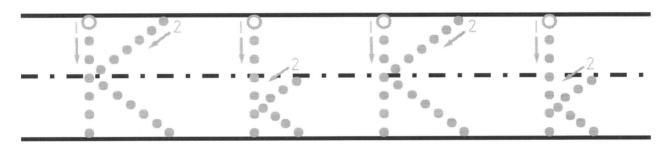

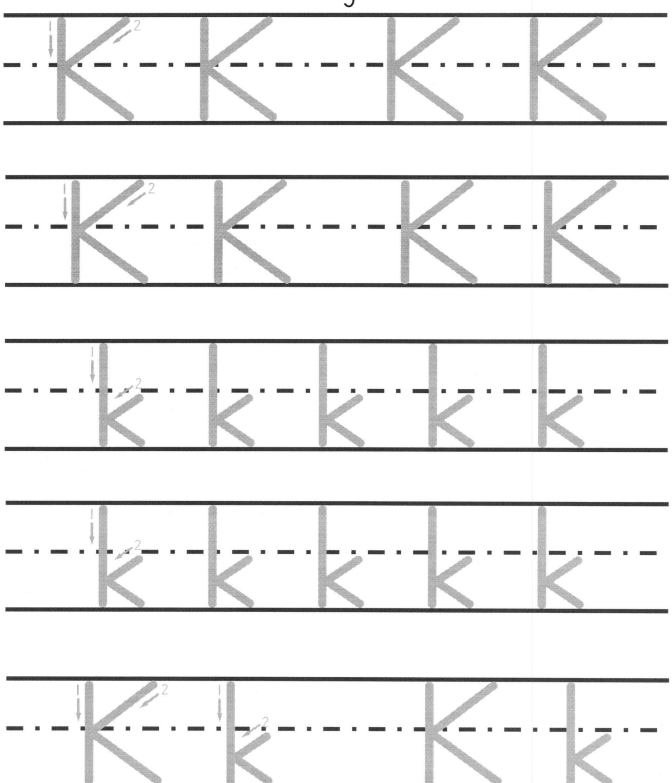

Connect the dots. What did you make?

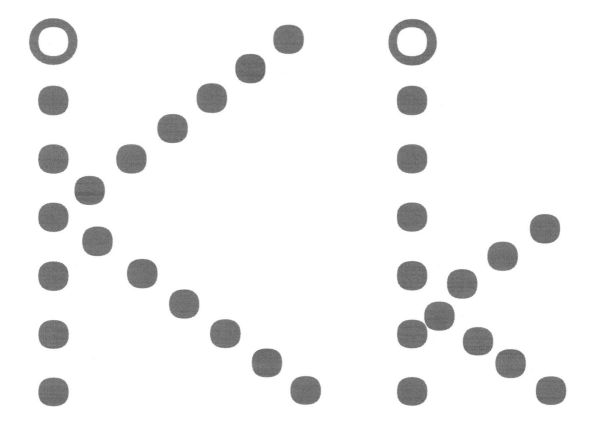

QUESTIONS TO ASK:

1. Who is married to the queen?
2. What do you get from your mom when she tucks you into bed at night? HINT: It goes with a hug.
3. What animal carries its baby in a pouch?
4. What sound does the letter K make?

Ll

LESSON

- ➢ Introduce the name and sound of the letter L. Read the italicized words.
  Answers: *(l sounds like /l/ as in lamp, lollipop, leg, and lemon)*
- ➢ Have your student repeat the letter sound several times.
- ➢ Have your student trace the uppercase and lowercase letters.

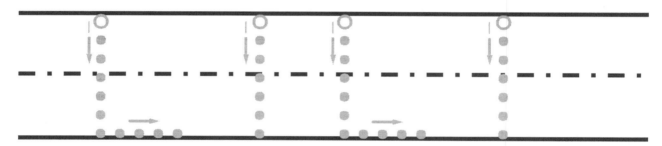

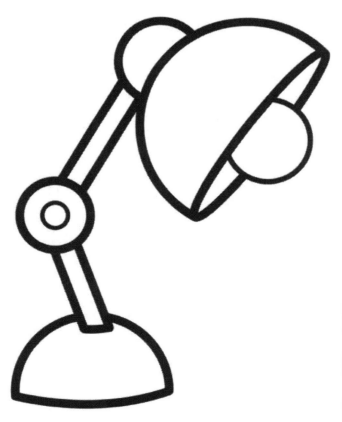

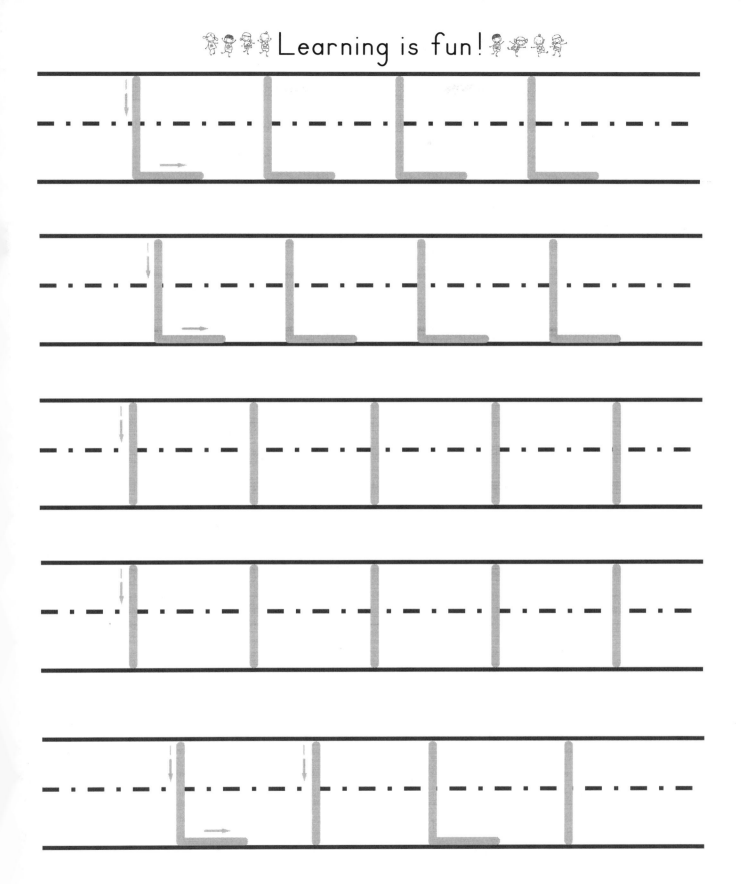

Connect the dots. What did you make?

QUESTIONS TO ASK:

1. What helps you seen in the dark and begins with the letter L?
2. What is Lazy Larry licking in the picture above?
3. What is connected to your foot and begins with an L?
4. What sound does the letter L make?

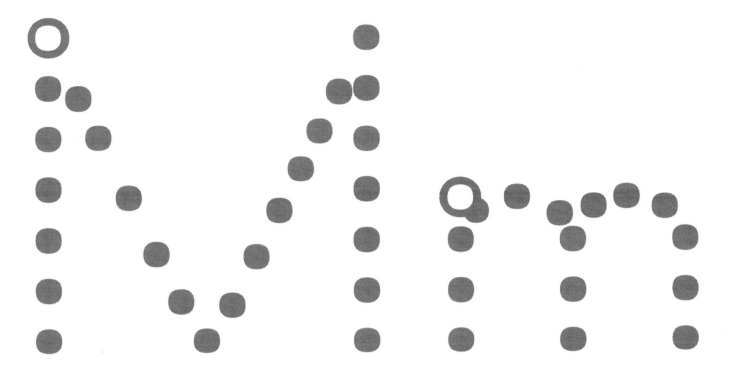

Connect the dots. What did you make?

QUESTIONS TO ASK:

1. What shines in the sky at night?
2. Who do you know whose name begins with the letter M?
3. Can you name an animal that begins with the letter M?
4. What sound does the letter M make?

Nn

LESSON

➤ Introduce the name and sound of the letter N. Read the italicized words.
  Answers: *(n sounds like /n/ as in nest, nuts, numbers, and net)*

➤ Have your student repeat the letter sound several times.

➤ Have your student trace the uppercase and lowercase letters.

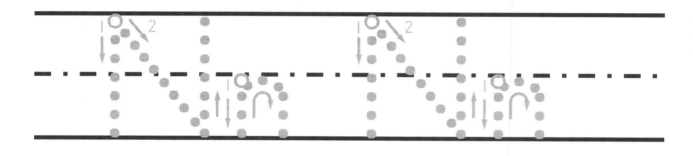

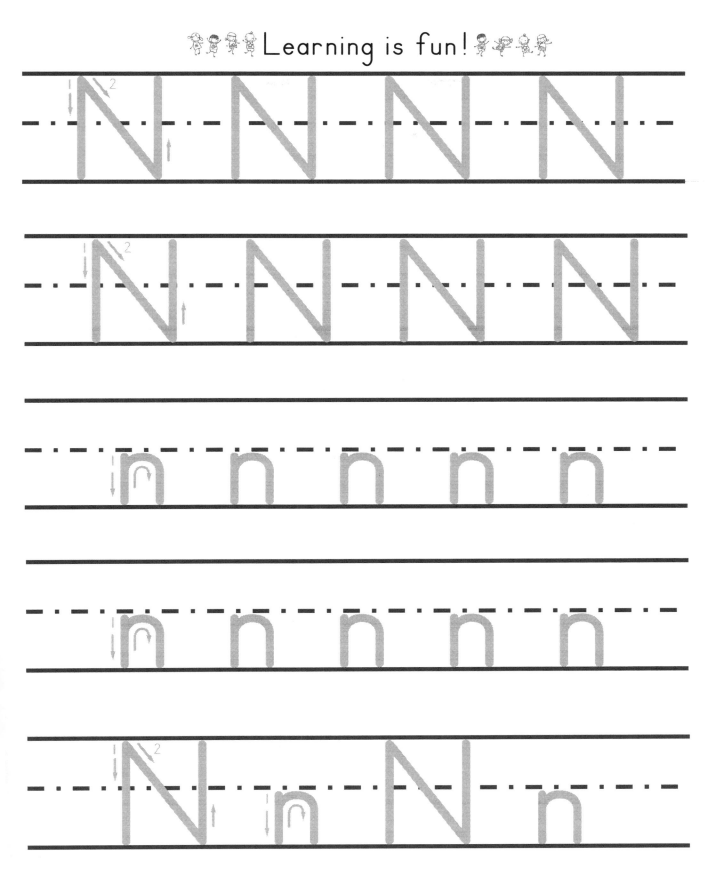

Connect the dots. What did you make?

QUESTIONS TO ASK:

1. Where do birds lay their eggs?
2. What do squirrels hide in trees?
3. What do you call these—1, 2, 3, 4, 5, 6, 7, 8, 9, 10?
4. What sound does the letter N make?

Connect the dots. What did you make?

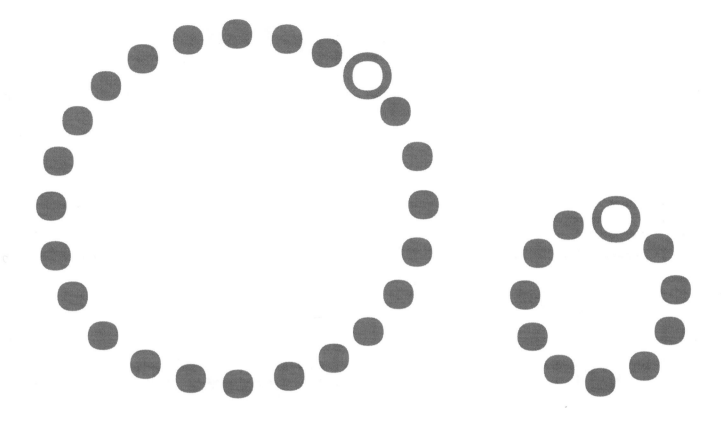

QUESTIONS TO ASK:

1. What animal has eight legs and lives in the ocean?
2. When you enter a room, what do you do to the lights? You turn them ___?
3. When you leave a room, what do you do to the lights? You turn them ___?
4. What sound does the letter O make?

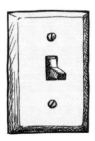

Pp

LESSON

➤ Introduce the name and sound of the letter P. Read the italicized words.
   Answers: *(p sounds like /p/ as in pink, purple, pizza, popcorn, and pig)*

➤ Have your student repeat the letter sound several times.

➤ Have your student trace the uppercase and lowercase letters.

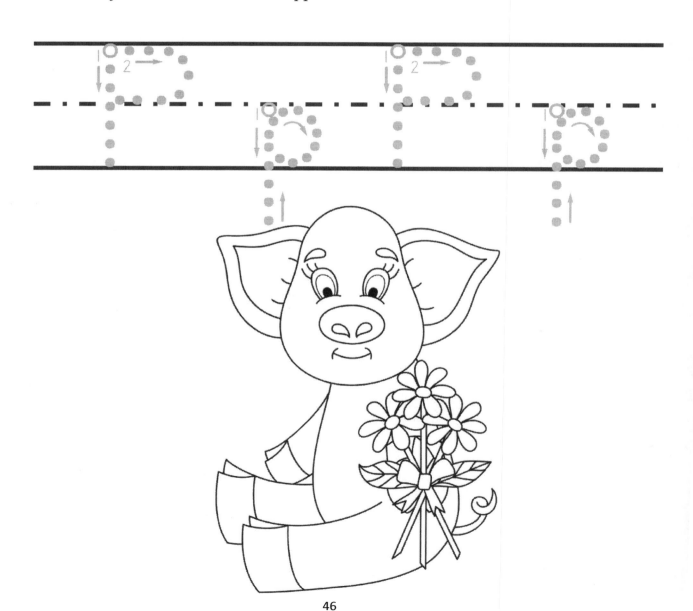

P P P P

P P P P

p p p p p

p p p p p

P P p

Connect the dots. What did you make?

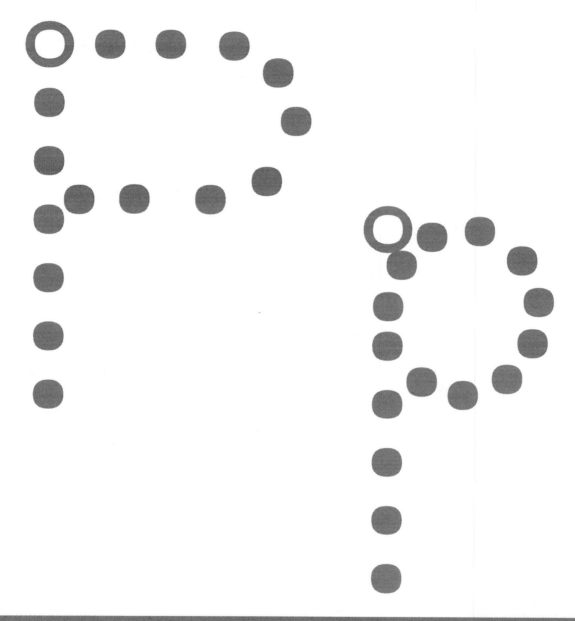

1. Name two colors that begin with the letter P.
2. What are two fun foods that begin with the letter P?
3. Name an animal that begins with the letter P.
4. What sound does the letter P make?

Qq

LESSON

➢ Introduce the name and sound of the letter Q. Read the italicized words.
Answers: *(q sounds like /kw/ as in quilt, queen, quit, and quiz)*

➢ Have your student repeat the letter sound several times.

➢ Have your student trace the uppercase and lowercase letters.

➢ Note: Q, in English, is always followed by the letter u.

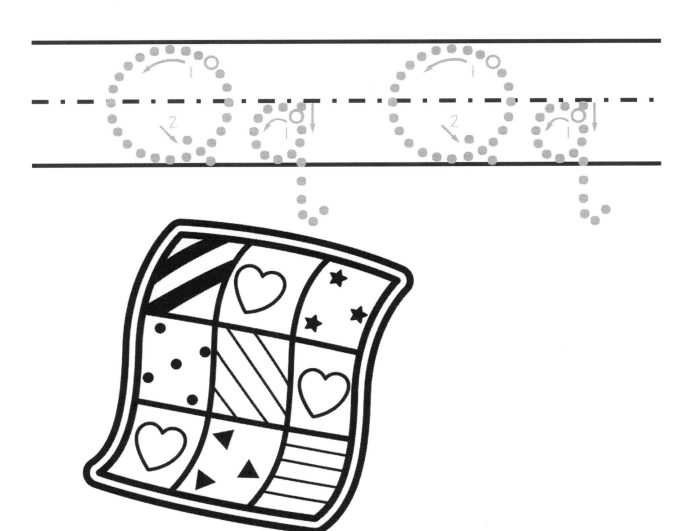

Q Q Q Q

Q Q Q Q

q q q q q

q q q q q

Q q Q q

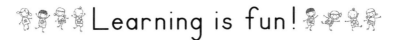

Connect the dots. What did you make?

QUESTIONS TO ASK:

1. What do we cover up with at night that starts with a Q?
2. Who is the king's wife?
3. What is another word for the word *stop* that begins with Q?
4. What sound does the letter Q make?

Rr

LESSON

➢ Introduce the name and sound of the letter R. Read the italicized words.
   Answers: *(r sounds like /r/ as in rabbit, red, ring, and rug)*

➢ Have your student repeat the letter sound several times.

➢ Have your student trace the uppercase and lowercase letters.

R R R R

R R R R

r r r r r r

r r r r r

R r R r

Connect the dots. What did you make?

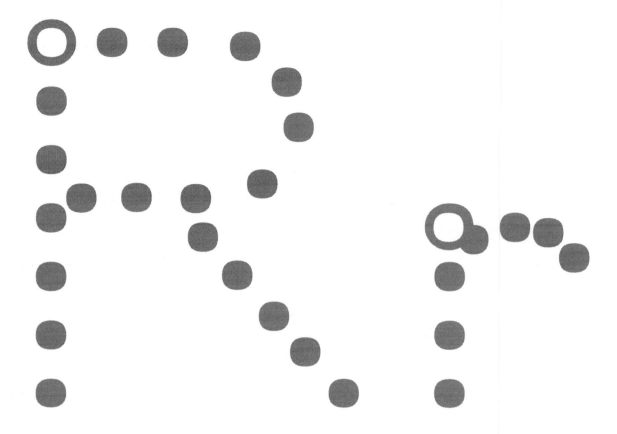

QUESTIONS TO ASK:

1. Name one color that begins with R.
2. What jewelry do people wear on their fingers?
3. What do you wipe your feet on when you enter the house?
4. What sound does the letter R make?

Ss

LESSON

- ➢ Introduce the name and sound of the letter S. Read the italicized words.
  Answers: *(s sounds like /s/ as in sun, sand, sit, and sad)*
- ➢ Have your student repeat the letter sound several times.
- ➢ Have your student trace the uppercase and lowercase letters.

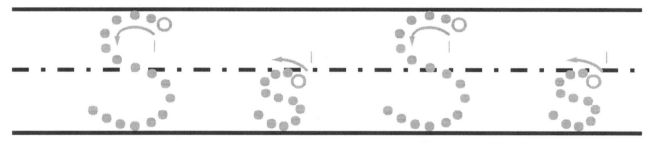

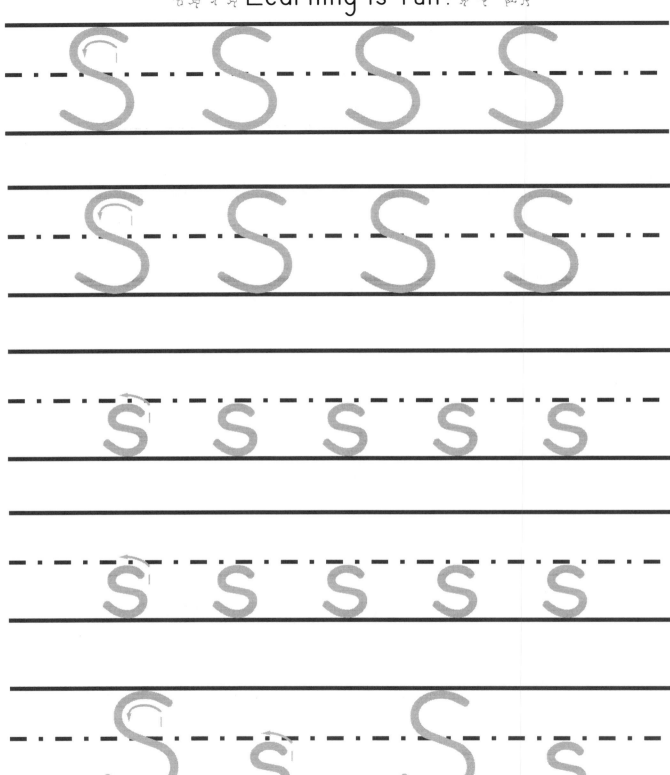

Uu

LESSON

➤ Introduce the name and short vowel sound of the letter U. Read the italicized words.
  Answers: *(u sounds like /ŭ/ as in umbrella, up, and under)*

➤ Have your student repeat the letter sound several times.

➤ Have your student trace the uppercase and lowercase letters.

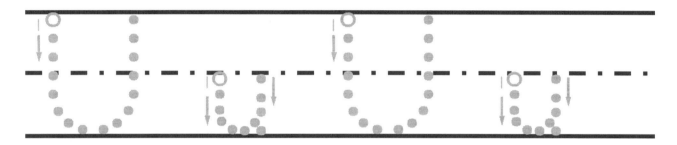

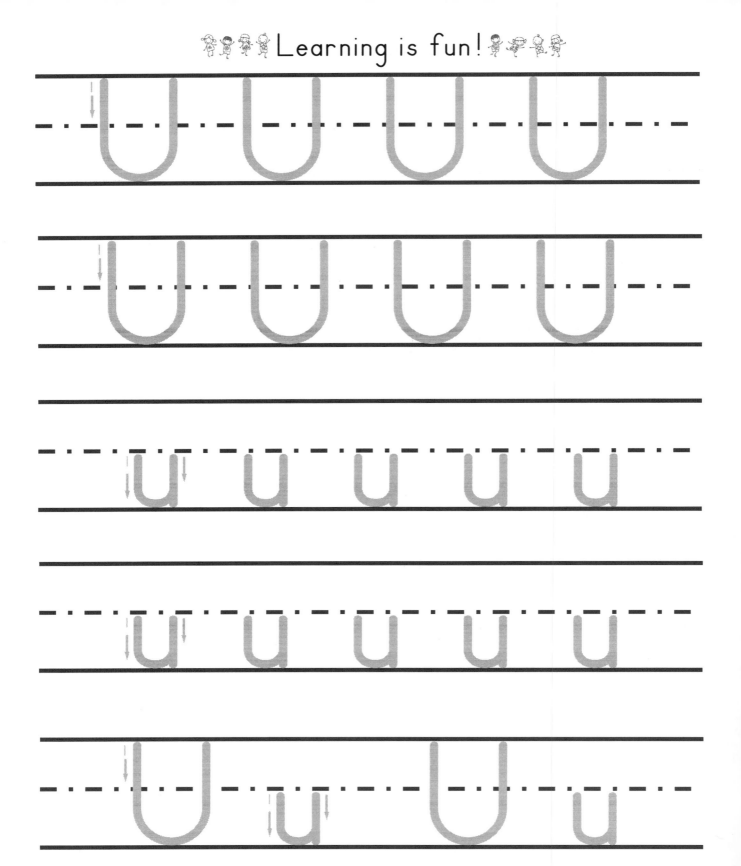

Connect the dots. What did you make?

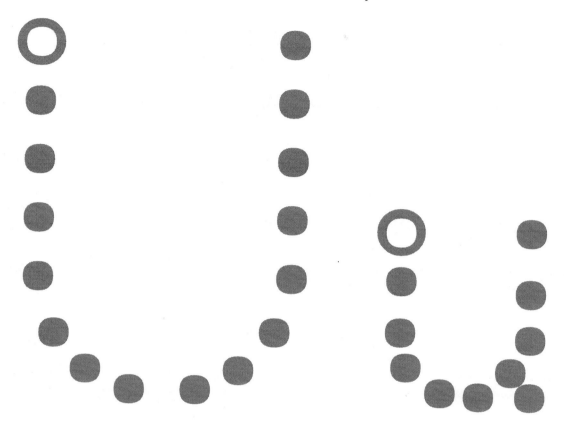

QUESTIONS TO ASK:

1. What do we use to keep the rain off of us?
2. What is the opposite of down?
3. What is the opposite of over?
4. What sound does the letter U make?

63

V v

LESSON

➢ Introduce the name and sound of the letter V. Read the italicized words.
   Answers: *(v sounds like /v/ as in vacuum, vegetables, and van)*

➢ Have your student repeat the letter sound several times.

➢ Have your student trace the uppercase and lowercase letters.

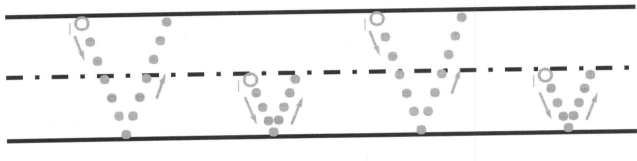

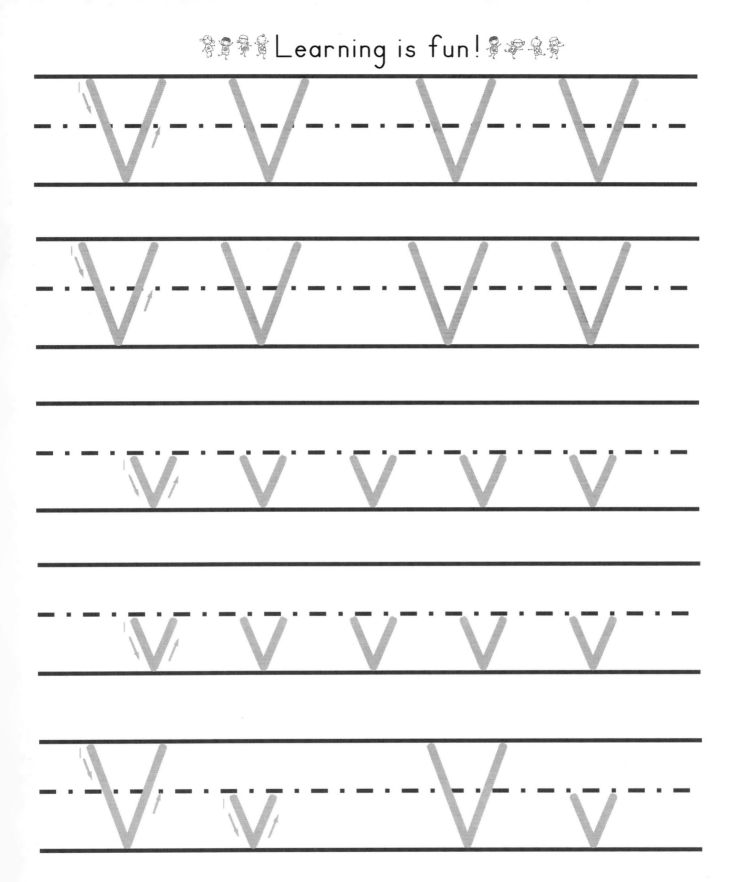

Connect the dots. What did you make?

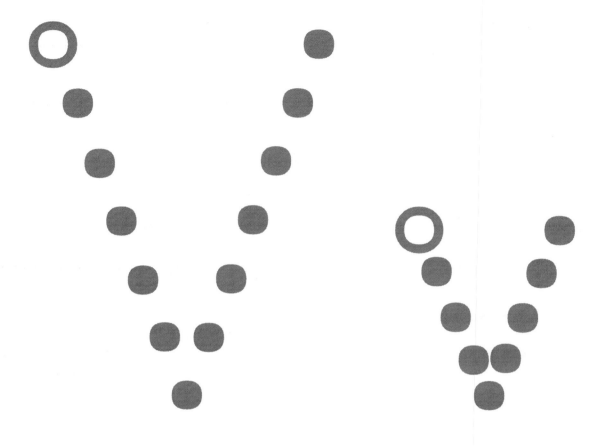

QUESTIONS TO ASK:

1. What do we use to clean the carpet?
2. To be healthy and strong we have to eat our fruits and _____?
3. What is a vehicle that a lot of people ride in? It's like a car but bigger.
4. What sound does the letter V make?

Ww

LESSON

- ➤ Introduce the name and sound of the letter W. Read the italicized words.
  Answers: *(w sounds like /w/ as in web, water, winter, and wasp)*
- ➤ Have your student repeat the letter sound several times.
- ➤ Have your student trace the uppercase and lowercase letters.

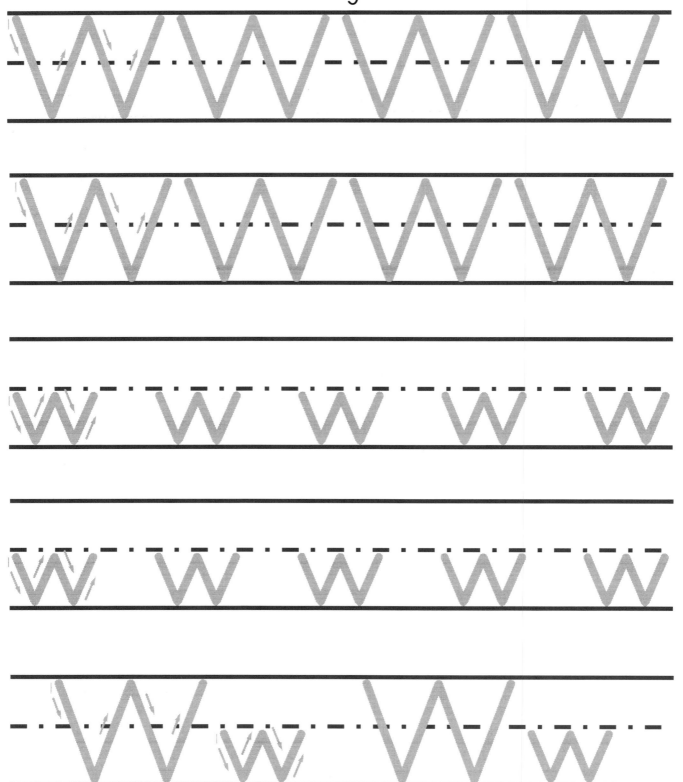

Connect the dots. What did you make?

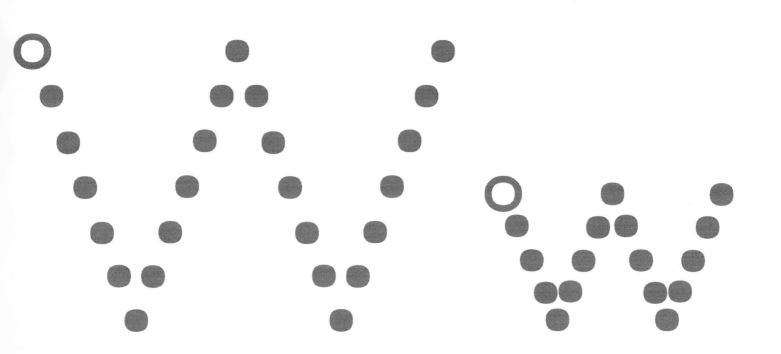

QUESTIONS TO ASK:

1. What letter comes after V in the alphabet?
2. What do fish live in?
3. In which season does it snow? Winter, spring, summer, or fall. It's _____ ?

4. What sound does the letter W make?

Xx

LESSON

➢ Since very few words begin with x, we are going to learn about words that end in x. Introduce the name and sound of the letter X.
 Read the italicized words. Answers: *(x sounds like /ks/ as in fox, six, box, and mix*

➢ Have your student repeat the letter sound several times.

➢ Have your student trace the uppercase and lowercase letters.

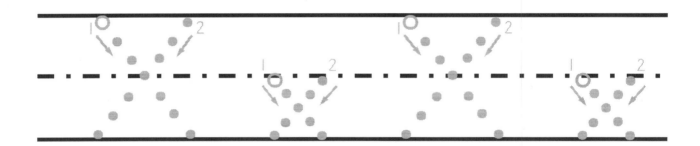

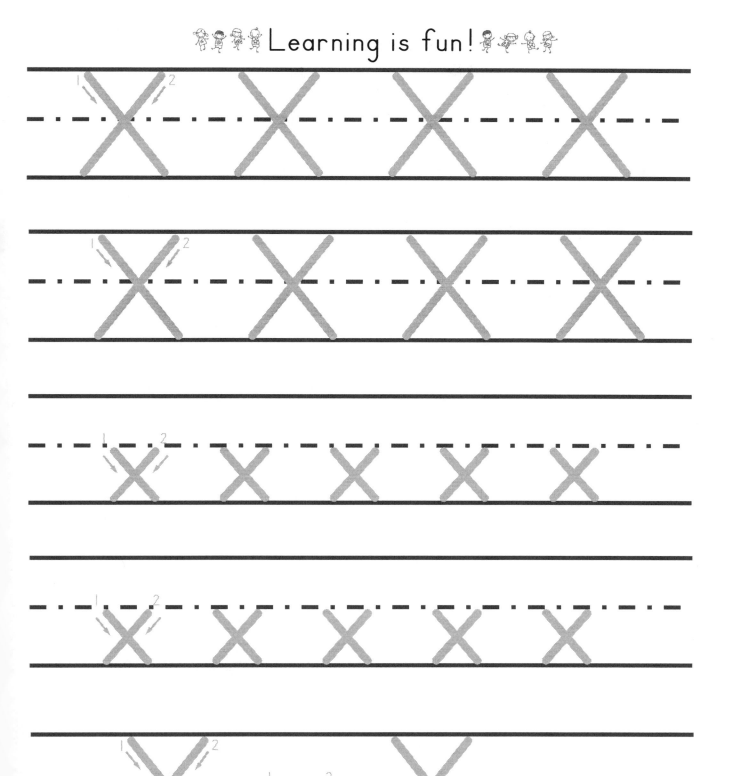

Connect the dots. What did you make?

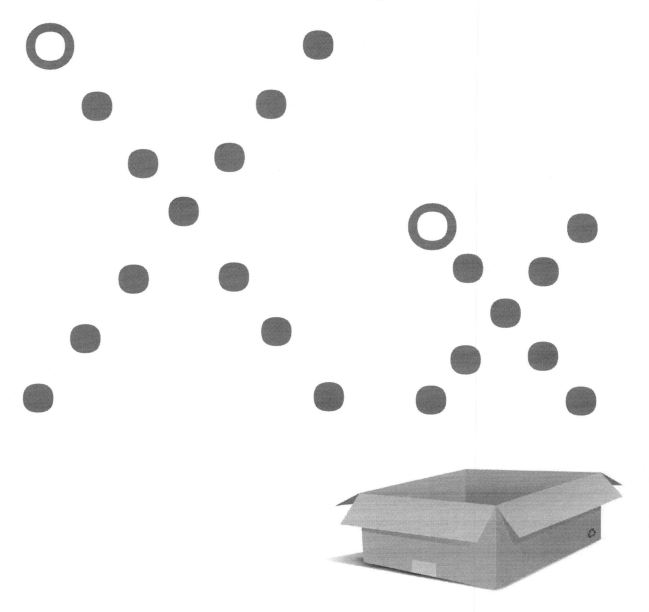

QUESTIONS TO ASK:

1. Since few words begin with x, we are going to talk about words that end in x. What is this number--6?
2. When you receive a present, what is it ususally inside of?
3. When you make a cake, what do you do to the ingedients. You use a fork or spoon.
4. What sound does the letter X make?

Y y

LESSON

➤ Introduce the name and sound of the letter Y. Read the italicized words.
  Answers: (*y sounds like /y/ as in yes, yak, yawn, and yarn*)

➤ Have your student repeat the letter sound several times.

➤ Have your student trace the uppercase and lowercase letters.

Y Y Y Y

Y Y Y Y

y y y y y

Y Y Y Y Y

Y y Y y

Connect the dots. What did you make?

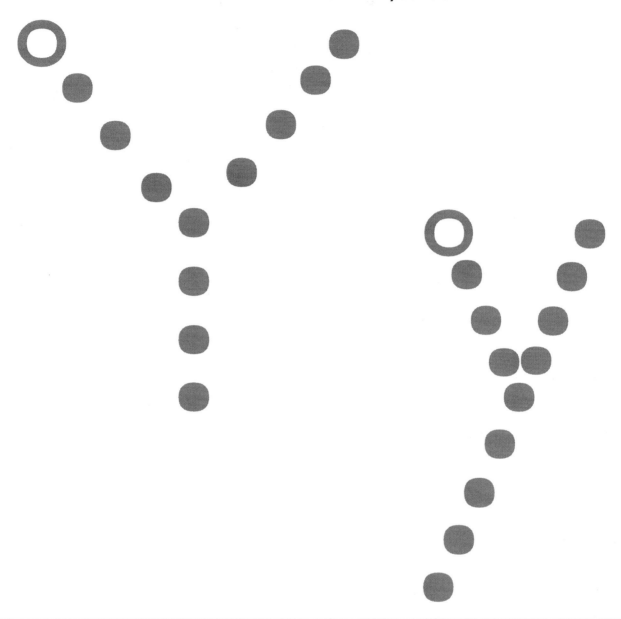

QUESTIONS TO ASK:

1. What is the opposite of no?
2. What is a big hairy animal that begins with y?
3. What do people do with their mouths when they are sleepy?
4. What sound does the letter Y make?

Zz

LESSON

➢ Introduce the name and sound of the letter Z. Read the italicized words.
   Answers: *(z sounds like / z / as in zipper, zebra, and zoo)*

➢ Have your student repeat the letter sound several times.

➢ Have your student trace the uppercase and lowercase letters.

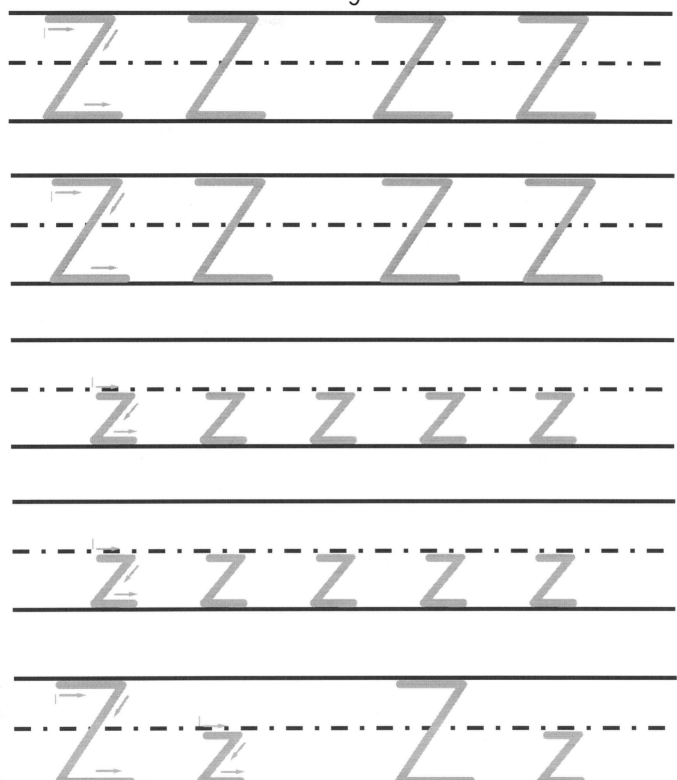

Connect the dots. What did you make?

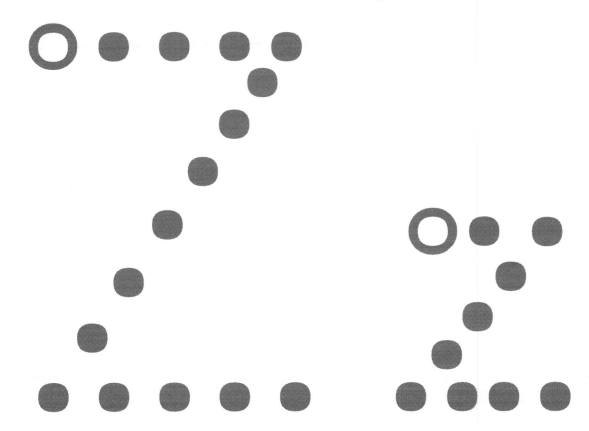

1. What do you use to close your jacket or jeans?
2. Name an animal that starts with a z.
3. Where in the city do you visit in order to see big animals?
4. What sound does the letter Z make?

Aa

ant

ant

ant

Bb

bear

bear

Cc

cat

cat

cat

Dd

dog

dog

dog

Ee

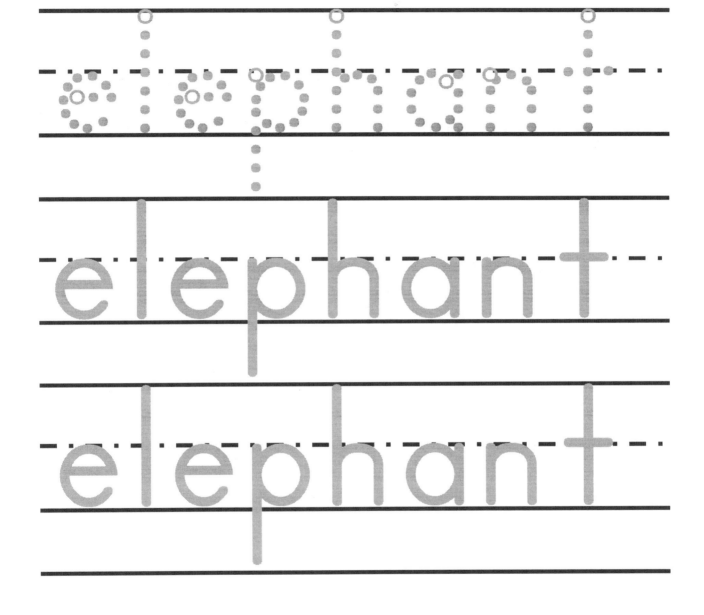

elephant

elephant

elephant

F f

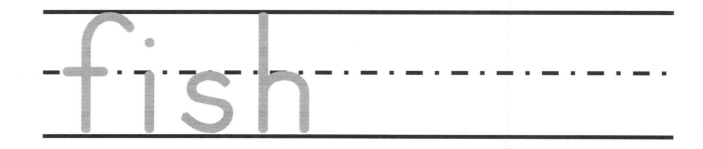

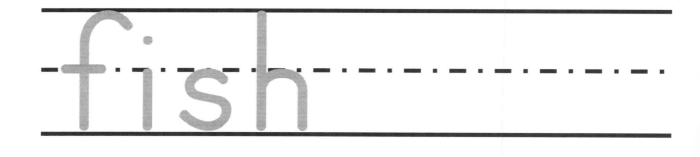

Gg

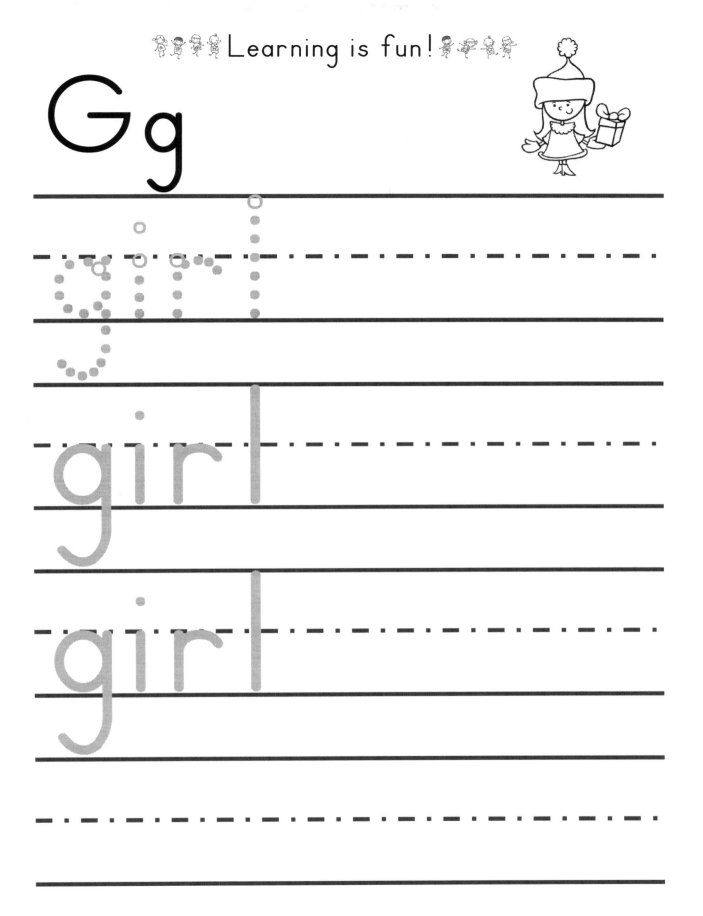

girl

girl

girl

girl

Hh

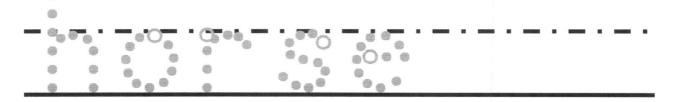

horse

horse

Ii

igloo

igloo

igloo

Jj

jellyfish

jellyfish

jellyfish

Kk

king

king

king

Ll

lamp

lamp

lamp

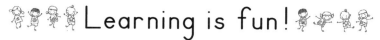

Mm

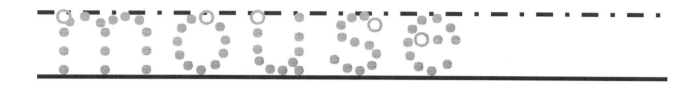

mouse

mouse

Nn

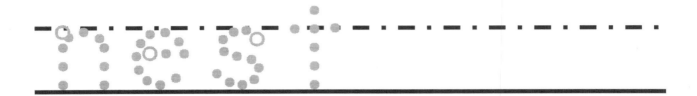

nest

nest

nest

Oo

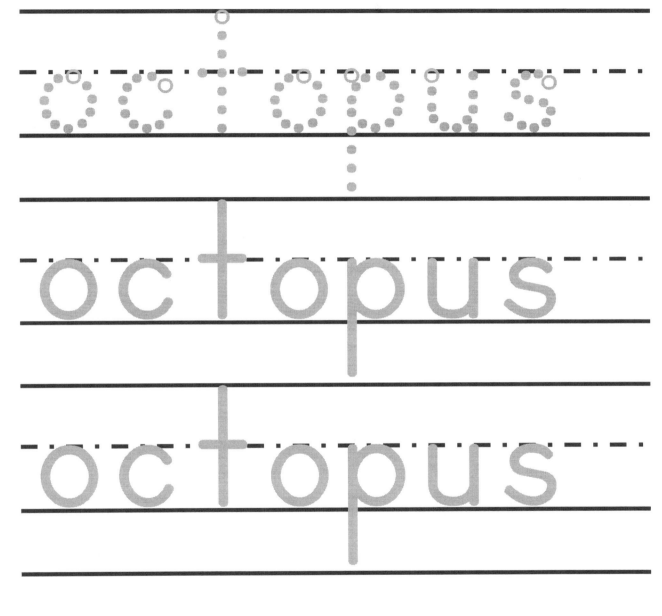

octopus

octopus

octopus

Pp

pig

pig

pig

Qq

quilt

quilt

quilt

Rr

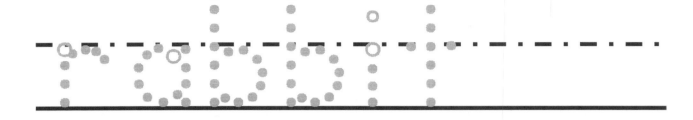

rabbit

rabbit

Ss

sun

sun

sun

Tt

turtle

turtle

turtle

Uu

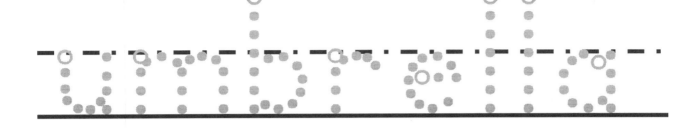

umbrella

umbrella

V v

vacuum

vacuum

Ww

web

web

Xx

fox

fox

fox

Y y

yak

yak

yak

Z z

ZOO

ZOO

Learning is fun!
Reproducible Alphabet Chart

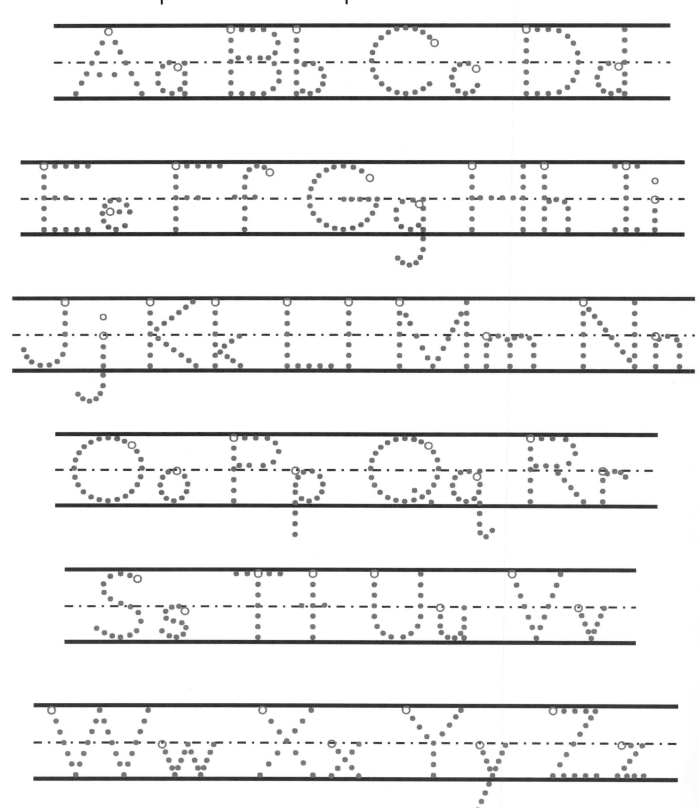

Made in the USA
Middletown, DE
17 February 2017